The Moments Journal

Pause | Reflect | Appreciate

"Life isn't a matter of milestones,

but of moments."

– Rose Kennedy

Written, Designed and Published by Nisha Kotecha.

Disclaimer:

While the author and publisher have made every effort to ensure that the information in this book was correct at the time of going to print, the author and publisher do not assume and hereby disclaim any liability to any party for any loss, damage, or disruption caused by errors or omissions, whether such errors or omissions result from negligence, accident, or any other cause. The advice and strategies contained herein may not be suitable for your situation. You should consult with a professional where appropriate.

ISBN number: 978-0-9956438-0-2

Printed in England, UK

FIRST EDITION

The Moments Journal

It's easy to get to the end of each day feeling tired and only remembering the big things that happened. But the small good things that happen in your day are worth remembering and cherishing.

The smile you exchanged with a stranger during a busy commute to work

The excitement you felt when you tried a new dish at your favourite restaurant

The calmness you felt after your yoga class

... All the nice moments, forgotten by the end of a busy day.

The world is full of amazing things. It's important for our well-being that we take the time to notice and be thankful for them.

I have created The Moments Journal to encourage you to remember your special moments and to help you feel happier over time as you create, notice and appreciate more and more of the good things in your day.

N. Kotecha

Nisha Kotecha,
Founder of The Moments Journal & Good News Shared

Connect with us!

Love The Moments Journal? Have a favourite question to answer each day? A suggestion to help us improve?

Please get in touch, we'd love to hear from you:

Instagram: @goodnewsmoments

Twitter: @goodnewsmoments

Facebook: @themomentsjournal

Email: hello@goodnewsshared.com

To receive uplifting inspirational stories by email once a fortnight sign up at www.goodnewsshared.com

IT'S TIME TO PAUSE, REFLECT and APPRECIATE

Read on for an explanation about how best to use your journal

"It is in your moments of decision that your destiny is shaped."

- Tony Robbins

PAUSE

When is the best time to fill in the journal?

Every night before you go to sleep.

Why do it in the evening?

A lot of people have a morning routine to help them get a good start to the day. It is important to end your day on a positive note too, to help you have a good night's sleep and so you feel happier the next day.

Plus, getting into the habit of revisiting your day is really useful: it helps you remember the moments you might have forgotten otherwise, and it helps you see what you enjoyed and what could be better for tomorrow.

How long will it take to fill in the journal?

This is completely up to you, and could change from day to day. It would be possible to write in the journal for a couple of minutes, but you could also spend fifteen minutes thinking and writing.

Creating good habits takes practice.

If you forget to write in your journal, don't feel guilty – fill it in there and then if you are at home, and do your best to remember to write in it again in the evening. The important thing is to start again as soon as you can.

Some tips to help you remember to write in your journal every day:

- Put your journal on your bedside table or close to your bed

- Keep a pen with your journal

- Set your alarm and brush your teeth after you have filled in your journal

- Tell your partner or a friend about it and ask them to see how it is going after a week. This will give you a friendly reminder if you haven't been filling the journal in, and if you have, it gives you a good opportunity to share how you are finding it

- Join The Moments Journal Online Community

The Moments Journal Online Community

"Unity is strength... when there is teamwork and collaboration, wonderful things can be achieved."

- Mattie Stepanek

If you would like to share thoughts and stories from your day in a kind, non-judgemental place and have the support and encouragement to keep your positive journaling habit up, The Moments Online Community is for you!

Visit www.goodnewsshared.com/journal-online-community to join for free.

REFLECT

Your nightly journal routine

If you have not given yourself the time to reflect on your day on a regular basis before, you might struggle to answer the questions at first.

On the surface the questions are simple, but they do require you to think about things that maybe you normally wouldn't.

If you cannot think of anything for a particular question, take the time to really think about your day – chances are you will remember something positive that you were otherwise going to forget.

If you still can't think of something from your day, maybe you can resolve to make sure you do something tomorrow that means you will be able to easily answer it that evening.

Start by writing the Date

The date has been left off on purpose. Each night, start by writing in the full date at the top of the page.

Every day is unique, even though sometimes each day can feel the same as the last. You get one shot at each day. As you write the date, remember to make the most of every moment you have.

What's the best news you heard today?

A potentially difficult question, but one really worth thinking about. It might seem like you do not hear good news every day. Newspapers tend to be full of bad news, and your friends and family don't have exciting things to share every day.

When answering the question, it doesn't have to be something big, or about you or someone you know.

Finding and hearing about good news is important. It reminds us that good things happen and there are good people in the world. Remembering and writing about it teaches your brain that it matters.

Also, studies have found hearing positive stories inspires people to act more altruistically.[1]

P.S. – if you are struggling to find some good news, head on over to www.goodnewsshared.com.

Plus, we've included some good news stories within the journal to inspire and motivate you, so look out for those.

Kindness

It's free. It feels amazing. We can all do it.

Research shows being kind to yourself and others is a simple way to avert the effects of stress.[2]

Not only will kind acts leave you feeling less stressed, studies have found that when people are on the receiving end of a good deed, they are more likely to carry one out for someone else.[3] So one act of kindness can result in a chain of kind acts!

This is why we encourage you to recall acts of kindness.

The kindest thing you did for someone else: This can be for someone you know or for a complete stranger. Take a look at the top 25 acts of kindness on the next page for some examples of kind acts that you might have forgotten you've done in your day.

The kindest thing you did for yourself: Again, this doesn't have to be something big, but it is important to remember to be kind to yourself. Eg. Having a relaxing bath, spending time writing in this journal, going to the gym. If you didn't do anything kind for yourself, try to remember to do something the next day, and every day after that!

The kindest thing someone did for you: recalling this happy moment from your day will lead you nicely into the gratitude question.

The top 25 acts of kindness carried out by people over three months[4]:

1. Holding the door open for a stranger
2. Giving directions to someone who looks lost
3. Stopping to let people cross the road
4. Letting someone with very little shopping go ahead in a queue
5. Putting money in a collection tin
6. Buying your partner their favourite food as a treat
7. Picking up something that someone has dropped
8. Letting a car out of a junction or driveway
9. Complimenting someone who isn't your partner on how they look
10. Giving spare change to a charity collector
11. Taking a spider outside instead of killing it
12. Telling someone about a great deal they could benefit from
13. Buying a gift for a friend or relative when it isn't their birthday
14. Telling a friend or relative you love them spontaneously
15. Offering to pick up items from a shop for someone else
16. Saying keep the change
17. Helping people reach for things high up on a shelf
18. Giving lifts without expecting payment
19. Picking up litter that someone else has dropped
20. Picking up clothes off the floor in shops
21. Offering a tissue
22. Giving a friend a lift to somewhere you weren't going
23. Putting the bins out for a neighbour
24. Telling someone there is something on their face / teeth
25. Picking up the bill as a treat

APPRECIATE

Gratitude

Psychologist Shawn Achor told Oprah that if you write down three things you are grateful for every day for 21 days in a row you train your brain to be optimistic.[5] Imagine the benefits if you do it every day for months or even years!

Gratitude has been found to have a positive effect on optimism levels and sleep quality, and reduces anxiety.[6]

When writing down what you are grateful for, the more specific you can be, the better, as it will help you relive the moment you are thinking of.

For example, instead of saying: *I am grateful for..*

My significant other; The weather; My friends

Try to go into more detail: *I am grateful for..*

My significant other cooking a lovely dinner tonight despite having had a long day at work

The weather being nice as it meant I was able to enjoy my walk to the station this morning

Working near my closest friends so we can meet for lunch regularly, like we did today!

Use the space below for any positive things you would like to remember from your day…

Draw, doodle, make a list, write one word that sums up your day and how you would like to remember it, leave it blank. It is completely up to you how you use the last part of the journal each day. You don't have to use it in the same way every day!

Why focus on the positives?

Shouldn't I think about the less good stuff in my day so I can learn from it?

While you are going through the questions each day you might remember the less good things from your day. And that's absolutely fine. We don't expect you to forget or ignore these parts of your day, but we don't encourage writing these things down in the journal.

Our minds tend to focus on and remember negative events more than positive ones, so by writing down some of the positive things from your day, every day, you are training your brain to realise that these things are important.[7]

Most people are often hard on themselves. We want to encourage people to remember and celebrate the good things from their day.

My Commitment To Journaling And Positivity

By writing in your journal regularly you will create a positive habit that trains your brain to see the good in each day, helping you feel happier and more motivated in the long term.

Studies have found that when we write down a commitment to do something we are more likely to persevere with it.[8]

So, with that in mind, make your commitment below:

I, ____,
commit to writing in The Moments Journal for at least 21 days in a row, starting ________________.

To help me make sure I fill in my journal every day I will (tick all that apply):

- O Leave my journal by my bed
- O Have a pen by my journal
- O Get ready for bed a few minutes earlier than normal, so I have time to write in my journal
- O Set my morning alarm afterwards
- O Brush my teeth after writing in my journal
- O Tell a friend or partner about the journal

**** A real life example from Nisha Kotecha's day ****

Date: 5th September 2016

What is the best news you heard today?

Giant pandas are no longer endangered!

Today, what is the kindest thing:

(a) someone did for you?

My husband made bean burgers because he knows how much I love them!

(b) you did for someone?

Let someone with less shopping go in front of me in the queue at the supermarket

(c) you did for yourself?

Made time to read before going to sleep

What are you grateful for?

Having some flexibility in when and where I work, my husband making the time to help me with a work project today, having the Internet so I can keep in touch with friends and family.

Use the space below for any positive things you would like to remember from your day…

Really enjoyed watching the movie Face/Off for the first time!

LET'S GET STARTED

"Cherish all your happy moments; they make a fine cushion for old age."

– Booth Tarkington

Date:

What is the best news you heard today?

Today, what is the kindest thing:
(a) someone did for you?

(b) you did for someone?

(c) you did for yourself?

What are you grateful for?

Use the space below for any positive things you would like to remember from your day...

Date:

What is the best news you heard today?

Today, what is the kindest thing:
(a) someone did for you?

(b) you did for someone?

(c) you did for yourself?

What are you grateful for?

Use the space below for any positive things you would like to remember from your day...

Date:

What is the best news you heard today?

Today, what is the kindest thing:
(a) someone did for you?

(b) you did for someone?

(c) you did for yourself?

What are you grateful for?

Use the space below for any positive things you would like to remember from your day…

Date:

What is the best news you heard today?

Today, what is the kindest thing:
(a) someone did for you?

(b) you did for someone?

(c) you did for yourself?

What are you grateful for?

Use the space below for any positive things you would like to remember from your day…

Date:

What is the best news you heard today?

Today, what is the kindest thing:
(a) someone did for you?

(b) you did for someone?

(c) you did for yourself?

What are you grateful for?

Use the space below for any positive things you would like to remember from your day…

Date:

What is the best news you heard today?

Today, what is the kindest thing:
(a) someone did for you?

(b) you did for someone?

(c) you did for yourself?

What are you grateful for?

Use the space below for any positive things you would like to remember from your day…

Date:

What is the best news you heard today?

Today, what is the kindest thing:
(a) someone did for you?

(b) you did for someone?

(c) you did for yourself?

What are you grateful for?

Use the space below for any positive things you would like to remember from your day…

Date:

What is the best news you heard today?

Today, what is the kindest thing:
(a) someone did for you?

(b) you did for someone?

(c) you did for yourself?

What are you grateful for?

Use the space below for any positive things you would like to remember from your day…

Date:

What is the best news you heard today?

Today, what is the kindest thing:
(a) someone did for you?

(b) you did for someone?

(c) you did for yourself?

What are you grateful for?

Use the space below for any positive things you would like to remember from your day…

Date:

What is the best news you heard today?

Today, what is the kindest thing:

(a) someone did for you?

(b) you did for someone?

(c) you did for yourself?

What are you grateful for?

Use the space below for any positive things you would like to remember from your day...

Date:

What is the best news you heard today?

Today, what is the kindest thing:

(a) someone did for you?

(b) you did for someone?

(c) you did for yourself?

What are you grateful for?

Use the space below for any positive things you would like to remember from your day...

Date:

What is the best news you heard today?

Today, what is the kindest thing:
(a) someone did for you?

(b) you did for someone?

(c) you did for yourself?

What are you grateful for?

Use the space below for any positive things you would like to remember from your day...

Date:

What is the best news you heard today?

Today, what is the kindest thing:
(a) someone did for you?

(b) you did for someone?

(c) you did for yourself?

What are you grateful for?

Use the space below for any positive things you would like to remember from your day...

Date:

What is the best news you heard today?

Today, what is the kindest thing:
(a) someone did for you?

(b) you did for someone?

(c) you did for yourself?

What are you grateful for?

Use the space below for any positive things you would like to remember from your day…

Date:

What is the best news you heard today?

Today, what is the kindest thing:

(a) someone did for you?

(b) you did for someone?

(c) you did for yourself?

What are you grateful for?

Use the space below for any positive things you would like to remember from your day…

Date:

What is the best news you heard today?

Today, what is the kindest thing:
(a) someone did for you?

(b) you did for someone?

(c) you did for yourself?

What are you grateful for?

Use the space below for any positive things you would like to remember from your day…

Date:

What is the best news you heard today?

Today, what is the kindest thing:
(a) someone did for you?

(b) you did for someone?

(c) you did for yourself?

What are you grateful for?

Use the space below for any positive things you would like to remember from your day...

Date:

What is the best news you heard today?

Today, what is the kindest thing:
(a) someone did for you?

(b) you did for someone?

(c) you did for yourself?

What are you grateful for?

Use the space below for any positive things you would like to remember from your day…

Date:

What is the best news you heard today?

Today, what is the kindest thing:

(a) someone did for you?

(b) you did for someone?

(c) you did for yourself?

What are you grateful for?

Use the space below for any positive things you would like to remember from your day...

Date:

What is the best news you heard today?

Today, what is the kindest thing:
(a) someone did for you?

(b) you did for someone?

(c) you did for yourself?

What are you grateful for?

Use the space below for any positive things you would like to remember from your day...

Date:

What is the best news you heard today?

Today, what is the kindest thing:

(a) someone did for you?

(b) you did for someone?

(c) you did for yourself?

What are you grateful for?

Use the space below for any positive things you would like to remember from your day...

Date:

What is the best news you heard today?

Today, what is the kindest thing:
(a) someone did for you?

(b) you did for someone?

(c) you did for yourself?

What are you grateful for?

Use the space below for any positive things you would like to remember from your day…

Date:

What is the best news you heard today?

Today, what is the kindest thing:
(a) someone did for you?

(b) you did for someone?

(c) you did for yourself?

What are you grateful for?

Use the space below for any positive things you would like to remember from your day...

Date:

What is the best news you heard today?

Today, what is the kindest thing:
(a) someone did for you?

(b) you did for someone?

(c) you did for yourself?

What are you grateful for?

Use the space below for any positive things you would like to remember from your day...

Date:

What is the best news you heard today?

Today, what is the kindest thing:
(a) someone did for you?

(b) you did for someone?

(c) you did for yourself?

What are you grateful for?

Use the space below for any positive things you would like to remember from your day…

Date:

What is the best news you heard today?

Today, what is the kindest thing:
(a) someone did for you?

(b) you did for someone?

(c) you did for yourself?

What are you grateful for?

Use the space below for any positive things you would like to remember from your day…

Date:

What is the best news you heard today?

Today, what is the kindest thing:
(a) someone did for you?

(b) you did for someone?

(c) you did for yourself?

What are you grateful for?

Use the space below for any positive things you would like to remember from your day…

Date:

What is the best news you heard today?

Today, what is the kindest thing:
(a) someone did for you?

(b) you did for someone?

(c) you did for yourself?

What are you grateful for?

Use the space below for any positive things you would like to remember from your day...

"No act of kindness, no matter how small, is ever wasted."

- Aesop

Student 'Sends a Smile' to Strangers Going Through Difficult Time

For the past three years a kind-hearted student has been sending uplifting messages, handwritten on postcards, to strangers who are going through difficult times.

The college student, who wishes to remain anonymous, sends touching handwritten letters to hospital wards, nursing homes and specialist treatment centres so staff can pass them directly on to individuals for whom the words of comfort and hope might bring a much-needed smile.

The letters include positive and hopeful messages such as:

'We may not know each other, but I wanted to remind you how special you are! The world is a brighter place for having you in it! I think you're amazing! Go out and spread your sunshine and I hope your life is filled with happiness, because you deserve it!'

The student said, ***"I don't know who will receive them, so they're not specific, but I hope that they are messages that people need to hear, and I like to think that they will help somebody. Most of the letters I write are just reminding people how special they are, how loved they are, how strong they are, etc."***

Date:

What is the best news you heard today?

Today, what is the kindest thing:
(a) someone did for you?

(b) you did for someone?

(c) you did for yourself?

What are you grateful for?

Use the space below for any positive things you would like to remember from your day...

Date:

What is the best news you heard today?

Today, what is the kindest thing:

(a) someone did for you?

(b) you did for someone?

(c) you did for yourself?

What are you grateful for?

Use the space below for any positive things you would like to remember from your day...

Date:

What is the best news you heard today?

Today, what is the kindest thing:
(a) someone did for you?

(b) you did for someone?

(c) you did for yourself?

What are you grateful for?

Use the space below for any positive things you would like to remember from your day...

Date:

What is the best news you heard today?

Today, what is the kindest thing:
(a) someone did for you?

(b) you did for someone?

(c) you did for yourself?

What are you grateful for?

Use the space below for any positive things you would like to remember from your day…

Date:

What is the best news you heard today?

Today, what is the kindest thing:
(a) someone did for you?

(b) you did for someone?

(c) you did for yourself?

What are you grateful for?

Use the space below for any positive things you would like to remember from your day...

Date:

What is the best news you heard today?

Today, what is the kindest thing:

(a) someone did for you?

(b) you did for someone?

(c) you did for yourself?

What are you grateful for?

Use the space below for any positive things you would like to remember from your day...

Date:

What is the best news you heard today?

Today, what is the kindest thing:

(a) someone did for you?

(b) you did for someone?

(c) you did for yourself?

What are you grateful for?

Use the space below for any positive things you would like to remember from your day…

Date:

What is the best news you heard today?

Today, what is the kindest thing:
(a) someone did for you?

(b) you did for someone?

(c) you did for yourself?

What are you grateful for?

Use the space below for any positive things you would like to remember from your day...

Date:

What is the best news you heard today?

Today, what is the kindest thing:
(a) someone did for you?

(b) you did for someone?

(c) you did for yourself?

What are you grateful for?

Use the space below for any positive things you would like to remember from your day…

Date:

What is the best news you heard today?

Today, what is the kindest thing:
(a) someone did for you?

(b) you did for someone?

(c) you did for yourself?

What are you grateful for?

Use the space below for any positive things you would like to remember from your day…

Date:

What is the best news you heard today?

Today, what is the kindest thing:
(a) someone did for you?

(b) you did for someone?

(c) you did for yourself?

What are you grateful for?

Use the space below for any positive things you would like to remember from your day…

Date:

What is the best news you heard today?

Today, what is the kindest thing:
(a) someone did for you?

(b) you did for someone?

(c) you did for yourself?

What are you grateful for?

Use the space below for any positive things you would like to remember from your day…

Date:

What is the best news you heard today?

Today, what is the kindest thing:
(a) someone did for you?

(b) you did for someone?

(c) you did for yourself?

What are you grateful for?

Use the space below for any positive things you would like to remember from your day…

Date:

What is the best news you heard today?

Today, what is the kindest thing:

(a) someone did for you?

(b) you did for someone?

(c) you did for yourself?

What are you grateful for?

Use the space below for any positive things you would like to remember from your day…

Date:

What is the best news you heard today?

Today, what is the kindest thing:
(a) someone did for you?

(b) you did for someone?

(c) you did for yourself?

What are you grateful for?

Use the space below for any positive things you would like to remember from your day...

Date:

What is the best news you heard today?

Today, what is the kindest thing:
(a) someone did for you?

(b) you did for someone?

(c) you did for yourself?

What are you grateful for?

Use the space below for any positive things you would like to remember from your day...

Date:

What is the best news you heard today?

Today, what is the kindest thing:
(a) someone did for you?

(b) you did for someone?

(c) you did for yourself?

What are you grateful for?

Use the space below for any positive things you would like to remember from your day…

Date:

What is the best news you heard today?

Today, what is the kindest thing:
(a) someone did for you?

(b) you did for someone?

(c) you did for yourself?

What are you grateful for?

Use the space below for any positive things you would like to remember from your day...

Date:

What is the best news you heard today?

Today, what is the kindest thing:

(a) someone did for you?

(b) you did for someone?

(c) you did for yourself?

What are you grateful for?

Use the space below for any positive things you would like to remember from your day...

Date:

What is the best news you heard today?

Today, what is the kindest thing:
(a) someone did for you?

(b) you did for someone?

(c) you did for yourself?

What are you grateful for?

Use the space below for any positive things you would like to remember from your day…

Date:

What is the best news you heard today?

Today, what is the kindest thing:

(a) someone did for you?

(b) you did for someone?

(c) you did for yourself?

What are you grateful for?

Use the space below for any positive things you would like to remember from your day…

Date:

What is the best news you heard today?

Today, what is the kindest thing:
(a) someone did for you?

(b) you did for someone?

(c) you did for yourself?

What are you grateful for?

Use the space below for any positive things you would like to remember from your day…

Date:

What is the best news you heard today?

Today, what is the kindest thing:
(a) someone did for you?

(b) you did for someone?

(c) you did for yourself?

What are you grateful for?

Use the space below for any positive things you would like to remember from your day…

Date:

What is the best news you heard today?

Today, what is the kindest thing:
(a) someone did for you?

(b) you did for someone?

(c) you did for yourself?

What are you grateful for?

Use the space below for any positive things you would like to remember from your day...

Date:

What is the best news you heard today?

Today, what is the kindest thing:
(a) someone did for you?

(b) you did for someone?

(c) you did for yourself?

What are you grateful for?

Use the space below for any positive things you would like to remember from your day…

Date:

What is the best news you heard today?

Today, what is the kindest thing:
(a) someone did for you?

(b) you did for someone?

(c) you did for yourself?

What are you grateful for?

Use the space below for any positive things you would like to remember from your day…

Date:

What is the best news you heard today?

Today, what is the kindest thing:
(a) someone did for you?

(b) you did for someone?

(c) you did for yourself?

What are you grateful for?

Use the space below for any positive things you would like to remember from your day...

Date:

What is the best news you heard today?

Today, what is the kindest thing:
(a) someone did for you?

(b) you did for someone?

(c) you did for yourself?

What are you grateful for?

Use the space below for any positive things you would like to remember from your day...

Date:

What is the best news you heard today?

Today, what is the kindest thing:
(a) someone did for you?

(b) you did for someone?

(c) you did for yourself?

What are you grateful for?

Use the space below for any positive things you would like to remember from your day...

Date:

What is the best news you heard today?

Today, what is the kindest thing:

(a) someone did for you?

(b) you did for someone?

(c) you did for yourself?

What are you grateful for?

Use the space below for any positive things you would like to remember from your day...

Date:

What is the best news you heard today?

Today, what is the kindest thing:

(a) someone did for you?

(b) you did for someone?

(c) you did for yourself?

What are you grateful for?

Use the space below for any positive things you would like to remember from your day…

Date:

What is the best news you heard today?

Today, what is the kindest thing:

(a) someone did for you?

(b) you did for someone?

(c) you did for yourself?

What are you grateful for?

Use the space below for any positive things you would like to remember from your day…

Date:

What is the best news you heard today?

Today, what is the kindest thing:
(a) someone did for you?

(b) you did for someone?

(c) you did for yourself?

What are you grateful for?

Use the space below for any positive things you would like to remember from your day...

Date:

What is the best news you heard today?

Today, what is the kindest thing:

(a) someone did for you?

(b) you did for someone?

(c) you did for yourself?

What are you grateful for?

Use the space below for any positive things you would like to remember from your day…

Date:

What is the best news you heard today?

Today, what is the kindest thing:

(a) someone did for you?

(b) you did for someone?

(c) you did for yourself?

What are you grateful for?

Use the space below for any positive things you would like to remember from your day...

Date:

What is the best news you heard today?

Today, what is the kindest thing:

(a) someone did for you?

(b) you did for someone?

(c) you did for yourself?

What are you grateful for?

Use the space below for any positive things you would like to remember from your day…

Date:

What is the best news you heard today?

Today, what is the kindest thing:
(a) someone did for you?

(b) you did for someone?

(c) you did for yourself?

What are you grateful for?

Use the space below for any positive things you would like to remember from your day…

Date:

What is the best news you heard today?

Today, what is the kindest thing:
(a) someone did for you?

(b) you did for someone?

(c) you did for yourself?

What are you grateful for?

Use the space below for any positive things you would like to remember from your day…

Date:

What is the best news you heard today?

Today, what is the kindest thing:
(a) someone did for you?

(b) you did for someone?

(c) you did for yourself?

What are you grateful for?

Use the space below for any positive things you would like to remember from your day…

Date:

What is the best news you heard today?

Today, what is the kindest thing:

(a) someone did for you?

(b) you did for someone?

(c) you did for yourself?

What are you grateful for?

Use the space below for any positive things you would like to remember from your day...

Date:

What is the best news you heard today?

Today, what is the kindest thing:

(a) someone did for you?

(b) you did for someone?

(c) you did for yourself?

What are you grateful for?

Use the space below for any positive things you would like to remember from your day…

Date:

What is the best news you heard today?

Today, what is the kindest thing:
(a) someone did for you?

(b) you did for someone?

(c) you did for yourself?

What are you grateful for?

Use the space below for any positive things you would like to remember from your day…

Date:

What is the best news you heard today?

Today, what is the kindest thing:
(a) someone did for you?

(b) you did for someone?

(c) you did for yourself?

What are you grateful for?

Use the space below for any positive things you would like to remember from your day...

Date:

What is the best news you heard today?

Today, what is the kindest thing:
(a) someone did for you?

(b) you did for someone?

(c) you did for yourself?

What are you grateful for?

Use the space below for any positive things you would like to remember from your day...

Date:

What is the best news you heard today?

Today, what is the kindest thing:

(a) someone did for you?

(b) you did for someone?

(c) you did for yourself?

What are you grateful for?

Use the space below for any positive things you would like to remember from your day…

Date:

What is the best news you heard today?

Today, what is the kindest thing:
(a) someone did for you?

(b) you did for someone?

(c) you did for yourself?

What are you grateful for?

Use the space below for any positive things you would like to remember from your day...

Date:

What is the best news you heard today?

Today, what is the kindest thing:

(a) someone did for you?

(b) you did for someone?

(c) you did for yourself?

What are you grateful for?

Use the space below for any positive things you would like to remember from your day…

"Everyone suffers some injustice in life, and what better motivation than to help others not suffer in the same way."

- Bella Thorne

Meet the Seven Year Old Cancer Survivor Who is Helping Other Young Cancer Survivors

At just two years old Erin Gentry was diagnosed with retinoblastoma, a rare form of eye cancer which affects babies and young children. She needed lifesaving surgery to remove her left eye and stop the cancer spreading, followed by chemotherapy.

Now, aged seven, the North Londoner has been given a prestigious award by the Childhood Eye Cancer Trust in recognition of the commitment she has shown in helping other young cancer survivors.

Erin spent over a year struggling to get to grips with wearing an artificial eye but since she mastered it she has dedicated her time to teaching other children at a special group called Eye Club, where some of the children are older than her.

Gemma Melisi, Play Specialist at the Royal London Hospital which hosts the Eye Club, and where Erin was diagnosed, said ***"Erin teaches all the children who are not confident with their artificial eye. She shows them how to clean their special eye and how to put it in and out. Erin is an amazing teacher and loves to help the other children. Without people like her, Eye Club simply wouldn't work."***

Date:

What is the best news you heard today?

Today, what is the kindest thing:

(a) someone did for you?

(b) you did for someone?

(c) you did for yourself?

What are you grateful for?

Use the space below for any positive things you would like to remember from your day…

Date:

What is the best news you heard today?

Today, what is the kindest thing:
(a) someone did for you?

(b) you did for someone?

(c) you did for yourself?

What are you grateful for?

Use the space below for any positive things you would like to remember from your day...

Date:

What is the best news you heard today?

Today, what is the kindest thing:
(a) someone did for you?

(b) you did for someone?

(c) you did for yourself?

What are you grateful for?

Use the space below for any positive things you would like to remember from your day...

Date:

What is the best news you heard today?

Today, what is the kindest thing:

(a) someone did for you?

(b) you did for someone?

(c) you did for yourself?

What are you grateful for?

Use the space below for any positive things you would like to remember from your day...

Date:

What is the best news you heard today?

Today, what is the kindest thing:
(a) someone did for you?

(b) you did for someone?

(c) you did for yourself?

What are you grateful for?

Use the space below for any positive things you would like to remember from your day...

Date:

What is the best news you heard today?

Today, what is the kindest thing:
(a) someone did for you?

(b) you did for someone?

(c) you did for yourself?

What are you grateful for?

Use the space below for any positive things you would like to remember from your day…

Date:

What is the best news you heard today?

Today, what is the kindest thing:
(a) someone did for you?

(b) you did for someone?

(c) you did for yourself?

What are you grateful for?

Use the space below for any positive things you would like to remember from your day…

Date:

What is the best news you heard today?

Today, what is the kindest thing:

(a) someone did for you?

(b) you did for someone?

(c) you did for yourself?

What are you grateful for?

Use the space below for any positive things you would like to remember from your day...

Date:

What is the best news you heard today?

Today, what is the kindest thing:
(a) someone did for you?

(b) you did for someone?

(c) you did for yourself?

What are you grateful for?

Use the space below for any positive things you would like to remember from your day…

Date:

What is the best news you heard today?

Today, what is the kindest thing:
(a) someone did for you?

(b) you did for someone?

(c) you did for yourself?

What are you grateful for?

Use the space below for any positive things you would like to remember from your day...

Date:

What is the best news you heard today?

Today, what is the kindest thing:
(a) someone did for you?

(b) you did for someone?

(c) you did for yourself?

What are you grateful for?

Use the space below for any positive things you would like to remember from your day...

Date:

What is the best news you heard today?

Today, what is the kindest thing:
(a) someone did for you?

(b) you did for someone?

(c) you did for yourself?

What are you grateful for?

Use the space below for any positive things you would like to remember from your day…

Date:

What is the best news you heard today?

Today, what is the kindest thing:
(a) someone did for you?

(b) you did for someone?

(c) you did for yourself?

What are you grateful for?

Use the space below for any positive things you would like to remember from your day...

Date:

What is the best news you heard today?

Today, what is the kindest thing:
(a) someone did for you?

(b) you did for someone?

(c) you did for yourself?

What are you grateful for?

Use the space below for any positive things you would like to remember from your day...

Date:

What is the best news you heard today?

Today, what is the kindest thing:
(a) someone did for you?

(b) you did for someone?

(c) you did for yourself?

What are you grateful for?

Use the space below for any positive things you would like to remember from your day…

Date:

What is the best news you heard today?

Today, what is the kindest thing:
(a) someone did for you?

(b) you did for someone?

(c) you did for yourself?

What are you grateful for?

Use the space below for any positive things you would like to remember from your day...

Date:

What is the best news you heard today?

Today, what is the kindest thing:
(a) someone did for you?

(b) you did for someone?

(c) you did for yourself?

What are you grateful for?

Use the space below for any positive things you would like to remember from your day...

Date:

What is the best news you heard today?

Today, what is the kindest thing:
(a) someone did for you?

(b) you did for someone?

(c) you did for yourself?

What are you grateful for?

Use the space below for any positive things you would like to remember from your day...

Date:

What is the best news you heard today?

Today, what is the kindest thing:
(a) someone did for you?

(b) you did for someone?

(c) you did for yourself?

What are you grateful for?

Use the space below for any positive things you would like to remember from your day…

Date:

What is the best news you heard today?

Today, what is the kindest thing:
(a) someone did for you?

(b) you did for someone?

(c) you did for yourself?

What are you grateful for?

Use the space below for any positive things you would like to remember from your day…

Date:

What is the best news you heard today?

Today, what is the kindest thing:
(a) someone did for you?

(b) you did for someone?

(c) you did for yourself?

What are you grateful for?

Use the space below for any positive things you would like to remember from your day...

Date:

What is the best news you heard today?

Today, what is the kindest thing:
(a) someone did for you?

(b) you did for someone?

(c) you did for yourself?

What are you grateful for?

Use the space below for any positive things you would like to remember from your day...

Date:

What is the best news you heard today?

Today, what is the kindest thing:
(a) someone did for you?

(b) you did for someone?

(c) you did for yourself?

What are you grateful for?

Use the space below for any positive things you would like to remember from your day...

Date:

What is the best news you heard today?

Today, what is the kindest thing:
(a) someone did for you?

(b) you did for someone?

(c) you did for yourself?

What are you grateful for?

Use the space below for any positive things you would like to remember from your day…

Date:

What is the best news you heard today?

Today, what is the kindest thing:
(a) someone did for you?

(b) you did for someone?

(c) you did for yourself?

What are you grateful for?

Use the space below for any positive things you would like to remember from your day…

Date:

What is the best news you heard today?

Today, what is the kindest thing:
(a) someone did for you?

(b) you did for someone?

(c) you did for yourself?

What are you grateful for?

Use the space below for any positive things you would like to remember from your day...

Date:

What is the best news you heard today?

Today, what is the kindest thing:
(a) someone did for you?

(b) you did for someone?

(c) you did for yourself?

What are you grateful for?

Use the space below for any positive things you would like to remember from your day…

Date:

What is the best news you heard today?

Today, what is the kindest thing:
(a) someone did for you?

(b) you did for someone?

(c) you did for yourself?

What are you grateful for?

Use the space below for any positive things you would like to remember from your day…

Date:

What is the best news you heard today?

Today, what is the kindest thing:
(a) someone did for you?

(b) you did for someone?

(c) you did for yourself?

What are you grateful for?

Use the space below for any positive things you would like to remember from your day…

Date:

What is the best news you heard today?

Today, what is the kindest thing:
(a) someone did for you?

(b) you did for someone?

(c) you did for yourself?

What are you grateful for?

Use the space below for any positive things you would like to remember from your day…

Date:

What is the best news you heard today?

Today, what is the kindest thing:
(a) someone did for you?

(b) you did for someone?

(c) you did for yourself?

What are you grateful for?

Use the space below for any positive things you would like to remember from your day…

Date:

What is the best news you heard today?

Today, what is the kindest thing:
(a) someone did for you?

(b) you did for someone?

(c) you did for yourself?

What are you grateful for?

Use the space below for any positive things you would like to remember from your day…

Date:

What is the best news you heard today?

Today, what is the kindest thing:
(a) someone did for you?

(b) you did for someone?

(c) you did for yourself?

What are you grateful for?

Use the space below for any positive things you would like to remember from your day...

Date:

What is the best news you heard today?

Today, what is the kindest thing:
(a) someone did for you?

(b) you did for someone?

(c) you did for yourself?

What are you grateful for?

Use the space below for any positive things you would like to remember from your day...

Date:

What is the best news you heard today?

Today, what is the kindest thing:
(a) someone did for you?

(b) you did for someone?

(c) you did for yourself?

What are you grateful for?

Use the space below for any positive things you would like to remember from your day...

Date:

What is the best news you heard today?

Today, what is the kindest thing:
(a) someone did for you?

(b) you did for someone?

(c) you did for yourself?

What are you grateful for?

Use the space below for any positive things you would like to remember from your day…

Date:

What is the best news you heard today?

Today, what is the kindest thing:
(a) someone did for you?

(b) you did for someone?

(c) you did for yourself?

What are you grateful for?

Use the space below for any positive things you would like to remember from your day…

Date:

What is the best news you heard today?

Today, what is the kindest thing:

(a) someone did for you?

(b) you did for someone?

(c) you did for yourself?

What are you grateful for?

Use the space below for any positive things you would like to remember from your day…

Date:

What is the best news you heard today?

Today, what is the kindest thing:
(a) someone did for you?

(b) you did for someone?

(c) you did for yourself?

What are you grateful for?

Use the space below for any positive things you would like to remember from your day...

Date:

What is the best news you heard today?

Today, what is the kindest thing:
(a) someone did for you?

(b) you did for someone?

(c) you did for yourself?

What are you grateful for?

Use the space below for any positive things you would like to remember from your day…

Date:

What is the best news you heard today?

Today, what is the kindest thing:

(a) someone did for you?

(b) you did for someone?

(c) you did for yourself?

What are you grateful for?

Use the space below for any positive things you would like to remember from your day...

Date:

What is the best news you heard today?

Today, what is the kindest thing:

(a) someone did for you?

(b) you did for someone?

(c) you did for yourself?

What are you grateful for?

Use the space below for any positive things you would like to remember from your day…

Date:

What is the best news you heard today?

Today, what is the kindest thing:

(a) someone did for you?

(b) you did for someone?

(c) you did for yourself?

What are you grateful for?

Use the space below for any positive things you would like to remember from your day...

Date:

What is the best news you heard today?

Today, what is the kindest thing:

(a) someone did for you?

(b) you did for someone?

(c) you did for yourself?

What are you grateful for?

Use the space below for any positive things you would like to remember from your day…

Date:

What is the best news you heard today?

Today, what is the kindest thing:
(a) someone did for you?

(b) you did for someone?

(c) you did for yourself?

What are you grateful for?

Use the space below for any positive things you would like to remember from your day…

Date:

What is the best news you heard today?

Today, what is the kindest thing:
(a) someone did for you?

(b) you did for someone?

(c) you did for yourself?

What are you grateful for?

Use the space below for any positive things you would like to remember from your day…

"Kindness is the best key to open the locked door of every heart."

- Debasish Mridha

"I want to do something nice for you today"

Mark Bustos works as a hair stylist in New York City for a salon with top celebrity clients.

Every Sunday – his only day off from work – he goes around New York City asking homeless people if they would like a free haircut.

He approaches each person with a simple phrase – "I want to do something nice for you today".

Knowing how people feel after a good haircut, Mark gives up to six homeless people a free hair cut every Sunday, and has done so for more than 200 consecutive weekends in a row.

He does it in open spaces and busy streets so people can watch and hopefully be inspired to also be kind to others who are less fortunate.

Mark decided to start offering free haircuts after a trip to the Philippines to visit family members, during which he rented a chair in a barbershop and gave free haircuts to impoverished local children.

Date:

What is the best news you heard today?

Today, what is the kindest thing:
(a) someone did for you?

(b) you did for someone?

(c) you did for yourself?

What are you grateful for?

Use the space below for any positive things you would like to remember from your day…

Date:

What is the best news you heard today?

Today, what is the kindest thing:
(a) someone did for you?

(b) you did for someone?

(c) you did for yourself?

What are you grateful for?

Use the space below for any positive things you would like to remember from your day…

Date:

What is the best news you heard today?

Today, what is the kindest thing:

(a) someone did for you?

(b) you did for someone?

(c) you did for yourself?

What are you grateful for?

Use the space below for any positive things you would like to remember from your day…

Date:

What is the best news you heard today?

Today, what is the kindest thing:

(a) someone did for you?

(b) you did for someone?

(c) you did for yourself?

What are you grateful for?

Use the space below for any positive things you would like to remember from your day…

Date:

What is the best news you heard today?

Today, what is the kindest thing:
(a) someone did for you?

(b) you did for someone?

(c) you did for yourself?

What are you grateful for?

Use the space below for any positive things you would like to remember from your day...

Date:

What is the best news you heard today?

Today, what is the kindest thing:
(a) someone did for you?

(b) you did for someone?

(c) you did for yourself?

What are you grateful for?

Use the space below for any positive things you would like to remember from your day…

Date:

What is the best news you heard today?

Today, what is the kindest thing:
(a) someone did for you?

(b) you did for someone?

(c) you did for yourself?

What are you grateful for?

Use the space below for any positive things you would like to remember from your day…

Date:

What is the best news you heard today?

Today, what is the kindest thing:
(a) someone did for you?

(b) you did for someone?

(c) you did for yourself?

What are you grateful for?

Use the space below for any positive things you would like to remember from your day...

Date:

What is the best news you heard today?

Today, what is the kindest thing:
(a) someone did for you?

(b) you did for someone?

(c) you did for yourself?

What are you grateful for?

Use the space below for any positive things you would like to remember from your day…

Date:

What is the best news you heard today?

Today, what is the kindest thing:
(a) someone did for you?

(b) you did for someone?

(c) you did for yourself?

What are you grateful for?

Use the space below for any positive things you would like to remember from your day…

Date:

What is the best news you heard today?

Today, what is the kindest thing:

(a) someone did for you?

(b) you did for someone?

(c) you did for yourself?

What are you grateful for?

Use the space below for any positive things you would like to remember from your day…

Date:

What is the best news you heard today?

Today, what is the kindest thing:
(a) someone did for you?

(b) you did for someone?

(c) you did for yourself?

What are you grateful for?

Use the space below for any positive things you would like to remember from your day…

Date:

What is the best news you heard today?

Today, what is the kindest thing:
(a) someone did for you?

(b) you did for someone?

(c) you did for yourself?

What are you grateful for?

Use the space below for any positive things you would like to remember from your day…

Date:

What is the best news you heard today?

Today, what is the kindest thing:
(a) someone did for you?

(b) you did for someone?

(c) you did for yourself?

What are you grateful for?

Use the space below for any positive things you would like to remember from your day…

Date:

What is the best news you heard today?

Today, what is the kindest thing:

(a) someone did for you?

(b) you did for someone?

(c) you did for yourself?

What are you grateful for?

Use the space below for any positive things you would like to remember from your day...

Date:

What is the best news you heard today?

Today, what is the kindest thing:
(a) someone did for you?

(b) you did for someone?

(c) you did for yourself?

What are you grateful for?

Use the space below for any positive things you would like to remember from your day…

Date:

What is the best news you heard today?

Today, what is the kindest thing:
(a) someone did for you?

(b) you did for someone?

(c) you did for yourself?

What are you grateful for?

Use the space below for any positive things you would like to remember from your day…

Date:

What is the best news you heard today?

Today, what is the kindest thing:
(a) someone did for you?

(b) you did for someone?

(c) you did for yourself?

What are you grateful for?

Use the space below for any positive things you would like to remember from your day…

Date:

What is the best news you heard today?

Today, what is the kindest thing:
(a) someone did for you?

(b) you did for someone?

(c) you did for yourself?

What are you grateful for?

Use the space below for any positive things you would like to remember from your day...

Date:

What is the best news you heard today?

Today, what is the kindest thing:
(a) someone did for you?

(b) you did for someone?

(c) you did for yourself?

What are you grateful for?

Use the space below for any positive things you would like to remember from your day…

Date:

What is the best news you heard today?

Today, what is the kindest thing:
(a) someone did for you?

(b) you did for someone?

(c) you did for yourself?

What are you grateful for?

Use the space below for any positive things you would like to remember from your day...

Date:

What is the best news you heard today?

Today, what is the kindest thing:
(a) someone did for you?

(b) you did for someone?

(c) you did for yourself?

What are you grateful for?

Use the space below for any positive things you would like to remember from your day...

Date:

What is the best news you heard today?

Today, what is the kindest thing:
(a) someone did for you?

(b) you did for someone?

(c) you did for yourself?

What are you grateful for?

Use the space below for any positive things you would like to remember from your day...

Date:

What is the best news you heard today?

Today, what is the kindest thing:
(a) someone did for you?

(b) you did for someone?

(c) you did for yourself?

What are you grateful for?

Use the space below for any positive things you would like to remember from your day…

Date:

What is the best news you heard today?

Today, what is the kindest thing:
(a) someone did for you?

(b) you did for someone?

(c) you did for yourself?

What are you grateful for?

Use the space below for any positive things you would like to remember from your day…

Date:

What is the best news you heard today?

Today, what is the kindest thing:
(a) someone did for you?

(b) you did for someone?

(c) you did for yourself?

What are you grateful for?

Use the space below for any positive things you would like to remember from your day…

Date:

What is the best news you heard today?

Today, what is the kindest thing:
(a) someone did for you?

(b) you did for someone?

(c) you did for yourself?

What are you grateful for?

Use the space below for any positive things you would like to remember from your day...

Date:

What is the best news you heard today?

Today, what is the kindest thing:
(a) someone did for you?

(b) you did for someone?

(c) you did for yourself?

What are you grateful for?

Use the space below for any positive things you would like to remember from your day...

Date:

What is the best news you heard today?

Today, what is the kindest thing:
(a) someone did for you?

(b) you did for someone?

(c) you did for yourself?

What are you grateful for?

Use the space below for any positive things you would like to remember from your day...

Date:

What is the best news you heard today?

Today, what is the kindest thing:

(a) someone did for you?

(b) you did for someone?

(c) you did for yourself?

What are you grateful for?

Use the space below for any positive things you would like to remember from your day…

Date:

What is the best news you heard today?

Today, what is the kindest thing:
(a) someone did for you?

(b) you did for someone?

(c) you did for yourself?

What are you grateful for?

Use the space below for any positive things you would like to remember from your day…

Date:

What is the best news you heard today?

Today, what is the kindest thing:
(a) someone did for you?

(b) you did for someone?

(c) you did for yourself?

What are you grateful for?

Use the space below for any positive things you would like to remember from your day...

Date:

What is the best news you heard today?

Today, what is the kindest thing:
(a) someone did for you?

(b) you did for someone?

(c) you did for yourself?

What are you grateful for?

Use the space below for any positive things you would like to remember from your day…

Date:

What is the best news you heard today?

Today, what is the kindest thing:

(a) someone did for you?

(b) you did for someone?

(c) you did for yourself?

What are you grateful for?

Use the space below for any positive things you would like to remember from your day...

Date:

What is the best news you heard today?

Today, what is the kindest thing:
(a) someone did for you?

(b) you did for someone?

(c) you did for yourself?

What are you grateful for?

Use the space below for any positive things you would like to remember from your day...

Date:

What is the best news you heard today?

Today, what is the kindest thing:
(a) someone did for you?

(b) you did for someone?

(c) you did for yourself?

What are you grateful for?

Use the space below for any positive things you would like to remember from your day…

Date:

What is the best news you heard today?

Today, what is the kindest thing:

(a) someone did for you?

(b) you did for someone?

(c) you did for yourself?

What are you grateful for?

Use the space below for any positive things you would like to remember from your day…

Date:

What is the best news you heard today?

Today, what is the kindest thing:
(a) someone did for you?

(b) you did for someone?

(c) you did for yourself?

What are you grateful for?

Use the space below for any positive things you would like to remember from your day...

Date:

What is the best news you heard today?

Today, what is the kindest thing:
(a) someone did for you?

(b) you did for someone?

(c) you did for yourself?

What are you grateful for?

Use the space below for any positive things you would like to remember from your day...

Date:

What is the best news you heard today?

Today, what is the kindest thing:
(a) someone did for you?

(b) you did for someone?

(c) you did for yourself?

What are you grateful for?

Use the space below for any positive things you would like to remember from your day…

Date:

What is the best news you heard today?

Today, what is the kindest thing:

(a) someone did for you?

(b) you did for someone?

(c) you did for yourself?

What are you grateful for?

Use the space below for any positive things you would like to remember from your day…

Date:

What is the best news you heard today?

Today, what is the kindest thing:

(a) someone did for you?

(b) you did for someone?

(c) you did for yourself?

What are you grateful for?

Use the space below for any positive things you would like to remember from your day…

Date:

What is the best news you heard today?

Today, what is the kindest thing:
(a) someone did for you?

(b) you did for someone?

(c) you did for yourself?

What are you grateful for?

Use the space below for any positive things you would like to remember from your day...

Date:

What is the best news you heard today?

Today, what is the kindest thing:
(a) someone did for you?

(b) you did for someone?

(c) you did for yourself?

What are you grateful for?

Use the space below for any positive things you would like to remember from your day…

Date:

What is the best news you heard today?

Today, what is the kindest thing:
(a) someone did for you?

(b) you did for someone?

(c) you did for yourself?

What are you grateful for?

Use the space below for any positive things you would like to remember from your day...

Date:

What is the best news you heard today?

Today, what is the kindest thing:

(a) someone did for you?

(b) you did for someone?

(c) you did for yourself?

What are you grateful for?

Use the space below for any positive things you would like to remember from your day…

Date:

What is the best news you heard today?

Today, what is the kindest thing:
(a) someone did for you?

(b) you did for someone?

(c) you did for yourself?

What are you grateful for?

Use the space below for any positive things you would like to remember from your day...

Good News!

You are close to finishing your journal. Head over to our website to order your new copy...

www.goodnewsshared.com/the-moments-journal

Date:

What is the best news you heard today?

Today, what is the kindest thing:
(a) someone did for you?

(b) you did for someone?

(c) you did for yourself?

What are you grateful for?

Use the space below for any positive things you would like to remember from your day...

Date:

What is the best news you heard today?

Today, what is the kindest thing:
(a) someone did for you?

(b) you did for someone?

(c) you did for yourself?

What are you grateful for?

Use the space below for any positive things you would like to remember from your day…

Date:

What is the best news you heard today?

Today, what is the kindest thing:
(a) someone did for you?

(b) you did for someone?

(c) you did for yourself?

What are you grateful for?

Use the space below for any positive things you would like to remember from your day...

Date:

What is the best news you heard today?

Today, what is the kindest thing:
(a) someone did for you?

(b) you did for someone?

(c) you did for yourself?

What are you grateful for?

Use the space below for any positive things you would like to remember from your day…

Date:

What is the best news you heard today?

Today, what is the kindest thing:
(a) someone did for you?

(b) you did for someone?

(c) you did for yourself?

What are you grateful for?

Use the space below for any positive things you would like to remember from your day…

Date:

What is the best news you heard today?

Today, what is the kindest thing:

(a) someone did for you?

(b) you did for someone?

(c) you did for yourself?

What are you grateful for?

Use the space below for any positive things you would like to remember from your day…

Date:

What is the best news you heard today?

Today, what is the kindest thing:
(a) someone did for you?

(b) you did for someone?

(c) you did for yourself?

What are you grateful for?

Use the space below for any positive things you would like to remember from your day...

Date:

What is the best news you heard today?

Today, what is the kindest thing:
(a) someone did for you?

(b) you did for someone?

(c) you did for yourself?

What are you grateful for?

Use the space below for any positive things you would like to remember from your day…

Date:

What is the best news you heard today?

Today, what is the kindest thing:
(a) someone did for you?

(b) you did for someone?

(c) you did for yourself?

What are you grateful for?

Use the space below for any positive things you would like to remember from your day...

Date:

What is the best news you heard today?

Today, what is the kindest thing:
(a) someone did for you?

(b) you did for someone?

(c) you did for yourself?

What are you grateful for?

Use the space below for any positive things you would like to remember from your day…

Date:

What is the best news you heard today?

Today, what is the kindest thing:
(a) someone did for you?

(b) you did for someone?

(c) you did for yourself?

What are you grateful for?

Use the space below for any positive things you would like to remember from your day...

Date:

What is the best news you heard today?

Today, what is the kindest thing:
(a) someone did for you?

(b) you did for someone?

(c) you did for yourself?

What are you grateful for?

Use the space below for any positive things you would like to remember from your day...

Date:

What is the best news you heard today?

Today, what is the kindest thing:
(a) someone did for you?

(b) you did for someone?

(c) you did for yourself?

What are you grateful for?

Use the space below for any positive things you would like to remember from your day…